The Berenstain Bears Meet Questron

ONE, TWO, THREE
HOW MANY WHEELS CAN YOU SEE?

By Stan & Jan Berenstain

Questron®

PRICE/STERN/SLOAN
Publishers, Inc., Los Angeles

DISTRIBUTED BY
RANDOM HOUSE, INC.
New York

A Bears-on-Wheels Jamboree! How many wheels will there be at the Bears-on-Wheels Jamboree?

ANNOUNCING A BEARS-ON-WHEELS JAMBOREE

THE QUESTRON® SYSTEM
COMBINING FUN WITH LEARNING

This book is part of **THE QUESTRON SYSTEM**, which offers children a unique aid to learning and endless hours of challenging entertainment.

The QUESTRON electronic ''wand'' uses a microchip to sense correct and incorrect answers with ''right'' or ''wrong'' sounds and lights. Victory sounds and lights reward the user when particular sets of questions or games are completed. Powered by a nine-volt alkaline battery, which is activated only when the wand is pressed on a page, QUESTRON should have an exceptionally long life. The QUESTRON ELECTRONIC WAND can be used with any book in the QUESTRON series.

ISBN: 0-394-89055-8

1 2 3 4 5 6 7 8 9 0

QUESTRON® is a trademark of Price/Stern/Sloan Publishers, Inc. U.S.A.
U.S. Patent 4,604,065; Patent 4,627,819; U.S. Patent Pending.
Canada Patented/Brevete 1984. International Patents Pending.
Printed in the United States of America.

HOW TO START QUESTRON

Hold **QUESTRON**
at this angle and
press the activator button
firmly on the page.

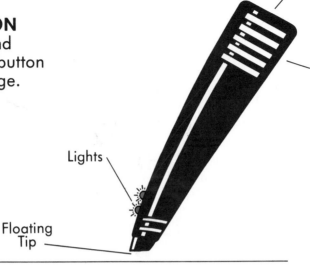

Battery Door
(When QUESTRON begins
to malfunction, add a new
9-volt alkaline battery.
To open battery door,
pull base up slightly
and slide out.)

Speaker

Lights

Floating
Tip

HOW TO USE QUESTRON

PRESS
Press **QUESTRON** firmly
on the shape below,
then lift it off.

TRACK
Press **QUESTRON** down on "Start"
and keep it pressed down
as you move to "Finish."

★ Start   Finish

RIGHT & WRONG WITH QUESTRON

Press **QUESTRON**
on the square.

See the green light and
hear the sound. This
green light and sound
say "You are correct."

Press **QUESTRON**
on the triangle.

The red light and sound
say "Try again." Lift
QUESTRON off the page and
wait for the sound to stop.

Press **QUESTRON**
on the circle.

Hear the victory sound.
Don't be dazzled
by the flashing lights.
You deserve them.

Going to the jamboree!
How many wheels can you see
going to the jamboree?

Skill: Simple counting

Press **Questron** on the correct answer
to each question.

The Bear family is going to the jamboree.
How many wheels are the Bears riding on?

9   7   10   12   8

Some wheels are <u>not</u> going to the jamboree.
How many wheels are <u>not</u> going?

6   5   9   10   7

How many wheels are there altogether?

10   9   13   15   20

5

START

10 MILES

7 MILES

6 MILES

9 MILES

5 MILES

7 MILES

The jamboree's 10 miles away.
Will the Bears find their way?
They'd better hurry—
the jamboree starts today!

The road to the jamboree is marked
with mile signs. If the Bears are
smart, they'll count backward from
10 to 1 on the mile signs and get
there in time for the fun. You will
too! Track **Questron** from start to finish.
Start on the ★.

There are lots of bears on lots of wheels.
Press **Questron** on the correct answer to each question.

How many bears are there?

6 5 8 7 9

How many wheels are there?

11 9 15 16 10

How many bears are wearing red shirts?

7 2 5 4 6

How many bears are wearing yellow shirts?

1 6 3 2 4

We're on more!
We're on more!

Press **Questron** on the correct number.

How many wheels are on two bicycles?

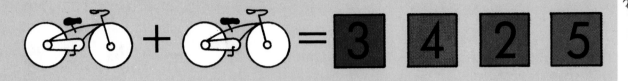

How many wheels are on one unicycle and one bicycle?

How many wheels are on one unicycle and two bicycles?

How many wheels are on two bicycles and one tricycle?

How many wheels are on three tricycles?

Said Cousin Fred,
"How about me?
I want to go
to the jamboree!

"I'll give my
brand-new bike a try.
Oh, me! Oh, my!
Oh, me! Oh, my!

"I do not like
the way it feels
to try to ride
on just two wheels!

"Ouch!" said Fred
as he hit the ground.
"Look—" said Mom,
"at these training wheels
I have found!"

When you put things together, you are <u>adding</u>.
The mark + means to add.
Press **Questron** on the correct number.

How many wheels were there on the bike after Fred's mom
<u>added</u> training wheels?

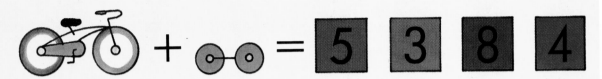 = 5 3 8 4

4 birds were watching when Fred tried to ride his new bike.
3 more birds came. How many birds watched altogether?

= 6 7 5 8

Fred's mom and dad watched him ride. 3 more bears came.
How many bears altogether watched him ride?

= 4 5 6

Taking away is called <u>subtracting</u>.
The mark **–** means to subtract or take away.
Press **Questron** on the correct number.

There were 7 birds watching when Fred fell down.
3 birds flew away. How many birds were left?

After a while Fred learned to ride his bicycle
and his mom took the training wheels off.
How many wheels were left?

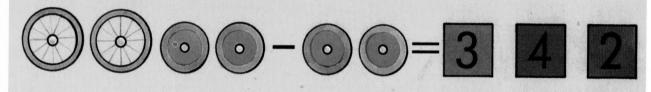

Here are some more subtracting problems to do.

6 frogs sat on a log. 4 frogs hopped away.
How many were left?

5 leaves grew on a branch. 3 leaves blew away.
How many were left?

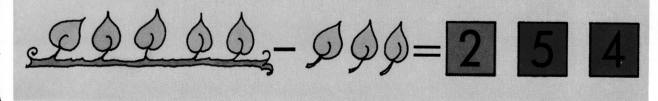

14

"Look at me!
Look at me!
I'm riding to
the jamboree!"

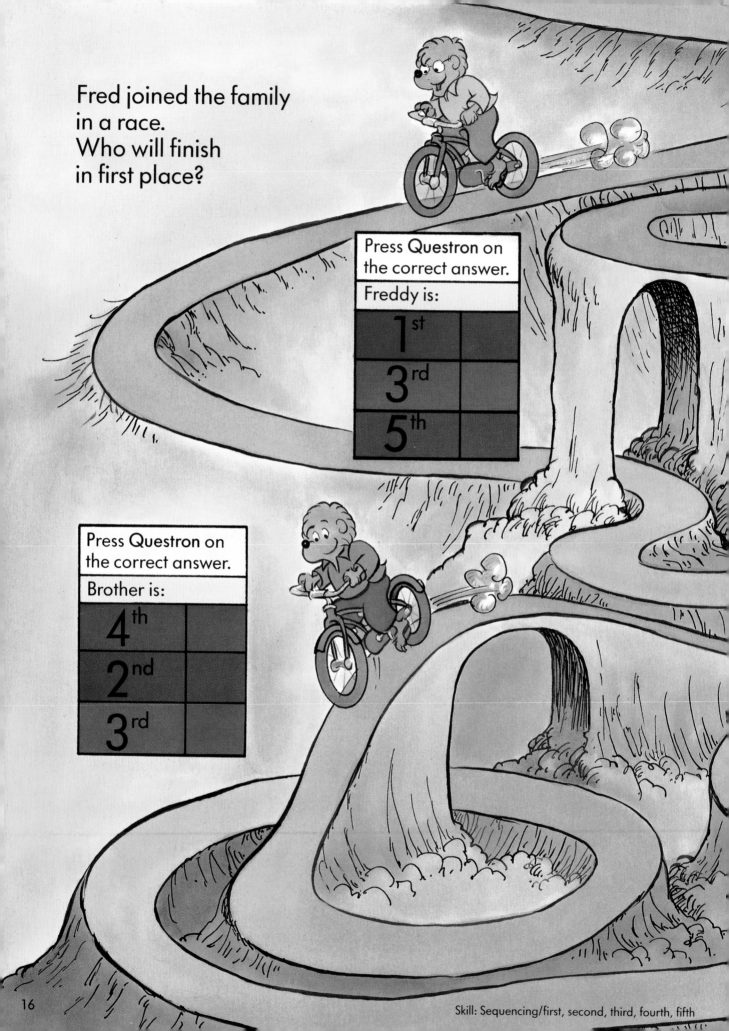

Fred joined the family
in a race.
Who will finish
in first place?

**Press Questron on
the correct answer.**

Freddy is:

1st	
3rd	
5th	

**Press Questron on
the correct answer.**

Brother is:

4th	
2nd	
3rd	

16

Skill: Sequencing/first, second, third, fourth, fifth

Press **Questron** on the correct answer.

Mama is:

5th	
4th	
3rd	

Press **Questron** on the correct answer.

Papa is:

5th	
2nd	
3rd	

FINISH LINE

Press **Questron** on the correct answer.

Sister is:

2nd	
1st	
3rd	

17

It's snack time
at the jamboree—
time out for
the family.

Time out for other
families, too.
"May we join you?"
"Yes! Please do!"

18

Other family groups are joining the Bear family for snack time. Each family has the same number of bears. When you put groups of the same size together to get a larger group, you are <u>multiplying</u>.
The mark x means to multiply.

Each family at the jamboree has 4 bears.
Press **Questron** on the correct answer.

How many bears will there be if 3 families get together?

3 x 🐻🐻🐻🐻 = 10 12 9

How many bears will there be if 2 families get together?

2 x 🐻🐻🐻🐻 = 6 14 8

How many bears will there be if 4 families get together?

4 x 🐻🐻🐻🐻 = 16 11 10

Another thing
there's going to be
is a grand parade
at the jamboree!

The bears divide
into twos.
Dividing is another skill
you can use.

When you break a larger group into smaller groups, each the same size, you are <u>dividing</u>.
The mark ÷ means to divide.

Press **Questron** on the correct number.

How many groups of 2 are there in a group of 6 bears?

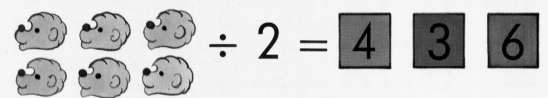 ÷ 2 = 4 3 6

How many groups of 2 are there in a group of 8 bears?

÷ 2 = 3 2 4

How many groups of 3 are there in a group of 6 bears?

÷ 3 = 2 3 4

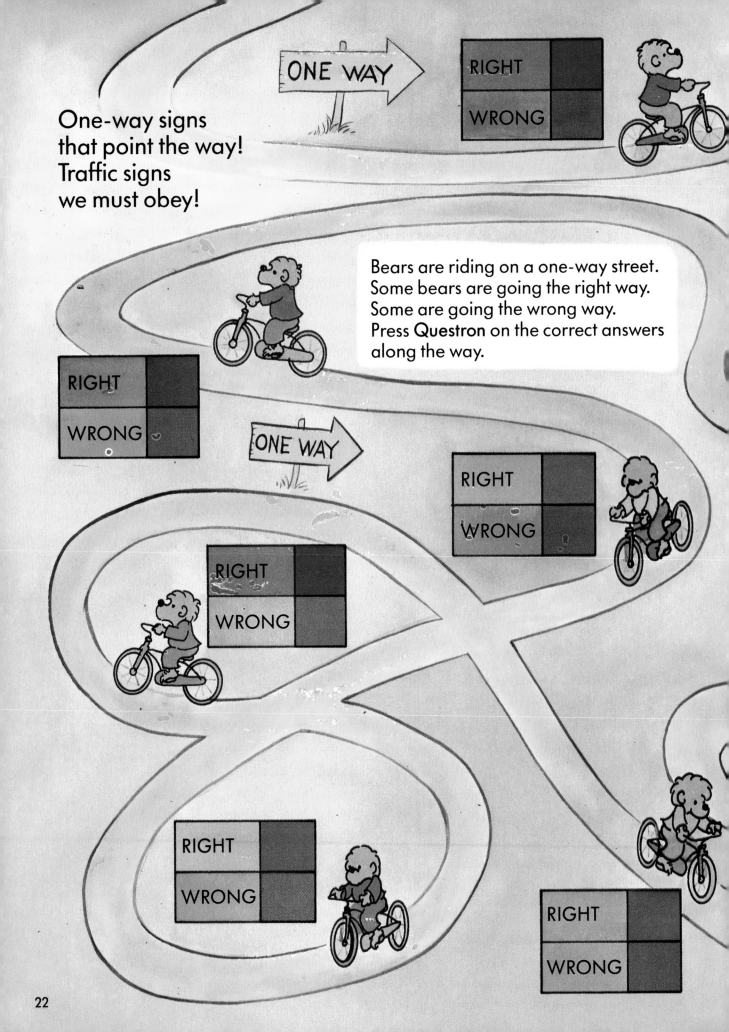

One-way signs
that point the way!
Traffic signs
we must obey!

Bears are riding on a one-way street.
Some bears are going the right way.
Some are going the wrong way.
Press **Questron** on the correct answers
along the way.

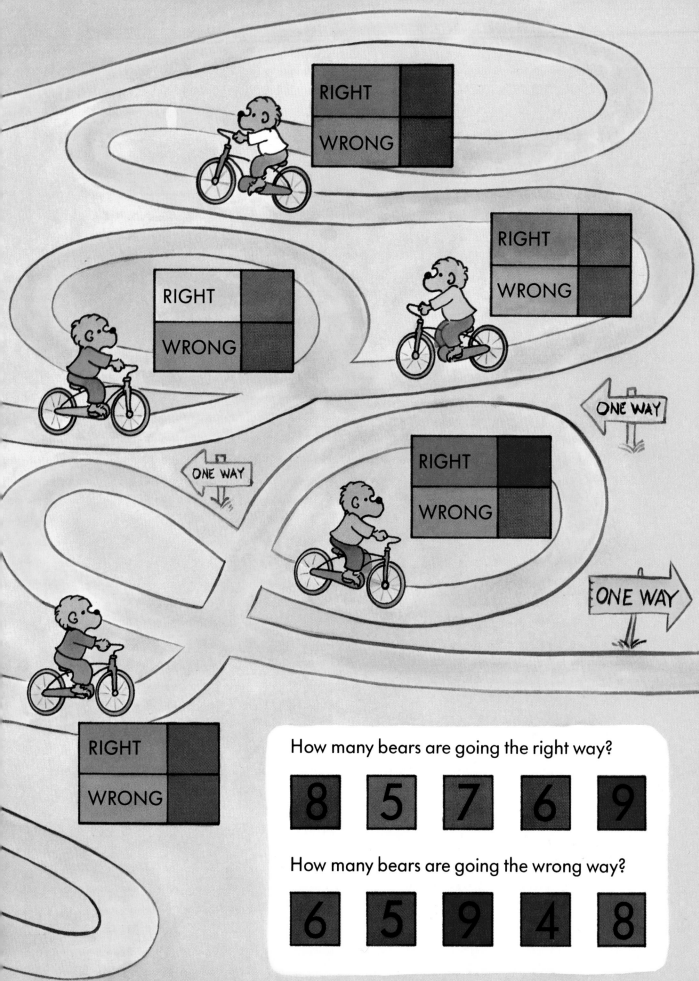

RIGHT
WRONG

RIGHT
WRONG

RIGHT
WRONG

ONE WAY

ONE WAY

RIGHT
WRONG

ONE WAY

RIGHT
WRONG

How many bears are going the right way?

8 5 7 6 9

How many bears are going the wrong way?

6 5 9 4 8

Look! Wheels on bears!
That's something new!
Wheels on bears
is something else
they can do!

Look up there!
Bears on wheels,
doing tricks!
One, two, three,
four, five, six
bears on wheels
doing tricks!

24

Press **Questron** on the correct answer.

How many bears are on how many wheels?

6 on 10	5 on 9	6 on 8
7 on 9	6 on 9	7 on 10

How many wheels on how many bears?

8 on 6	5 on 9	7 on 5
6 on 6	6 on 5	9 on 5

How many bears are on how many wheels?
Press **Questron** on the correct answers.

| 3 on 2 | 2 on 2 |
| 2 on 3 | 3 on 3 |

| 2 on 1 | 1 on 2 |
| 2 on 2 | 1 on 1 |

| 5 on 3 | 3 on 4 | 5 on 1 | 6 on 2 |
| 4 on 4 | 5 on 4 | 7 on 2 | 2 on 6 |

The Speedy Gang
races down the hill!
Will they crash?
If they don't stop,
they surely will!

8 on 9	9 on 8
8 on 10	10 on 8
7 on 10	6 on 9

Help! Help!
Bears off wheels!
Bears off wheels!
We do not like
the way it feels,
in a crash,
to be off wheels!

How many bears are off how many wheels?
Press **Questron** on the correct answer.

19 off 18	18 off 20
20 off 20	21 off 21
22 off 20	20 off 22

Press **Questron** on the correct answers.

When you say 2 + 2 = 4 you are…

| dividing | adding |
| subtracting | multiplying |

When you say 4 − 2 = 2 you are…

| dividing | adding |
| subtracting | multiplying |

When you say 2 x 2 = 4 you are…

| dividing | adding |
| subtracting | multiplying |

When you say 4 ÷ 2 = 2 you are…

| dividing | adding |
| subtracting | multiplying |

The jamboree was fun
and we happily admit
that with the help of Questron
we learned quite a bit.